D0294211

THE
Cath Kidston®
COLOURING
BOOK

THE

COLOURING
BOOK

quadrille

THE PRINT LIBRARY

Welcome to our Print Library! These are the 43 carefully selected, original designs that we've recreated in order over the following pages to inspire you to colour in. Use this Library for reference and inspiration as you reimagine the prints in new colourways or recreate the originals.

BIRTHDAY

**PARK
ROSE**

COWBOY

**BUTTON
ROSE**

STRAWBERRY

CRANHAM

**MINI
STANLEY**

| CANDY FLOWERS | BOAT | FRESTON ROSE | GUARDS |

| KENTISH ROSE | ANTIQUE ROSE BOUQUET | MUSHROOM | PROVENCE ROSE |

| DINO | KINGSWOOD ROSE | TEATIME | PATCHWORK |

CHELSEA FLOWERS   **LONDON BUSES**   **LITTLE BIRDS**   **ROYAL ROSE**

CIRCLE DITSY   **SHOOTING STARS**   **LACE STRIPE**   **BUDGIES**

PLANES   **CHICKEN**   **AUBREY ROSE**   **LONDON**

SQUIRRELS	FIRE ENGINES	CHERRIES	DAISY ROSE CHECK

BALLERINA	OUTER SPACE	RIVER FISH	FOLK FLOWERS

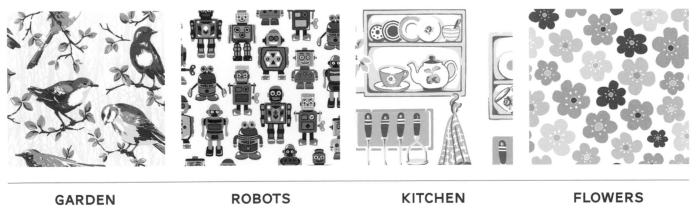

GARDEN BIRDS	ROBOTS	KITCHEN SCENE	FLOWERS

INTRODUCTION

Inspired by growing up in the British countryside and a love of vintage prints, Cath Kidston opened her first shop in West London in 1993. More than 20 years later, our design team still takes inspiration from quirky vintage finds, creating colourful, modern vintage prints to brighten up your day. Our beautifully detailed prints are designed in-house based on different themes and ideas and often include a nod to our British roots and cheeky sense of humour.

The *Cath Kidston Colouring Book* brings together a collection of 43 much-loved, classic designs from the Cath Kidston archive that have been carefully recreated for you to colour in. Reimagine your old favourites and create some new ones, from quirky novelties to iconic florals. We've even included a handy Print Library showing all the prints in their original colourways.

Colouring the *The Cath Kidston Colouring Book* will help to calm, relax and inspire you. Immerse yourself in the world of Cath Kidston prints and make our designs your own – it's the perfect outlet for your natural creativity.

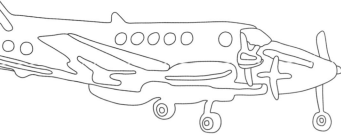
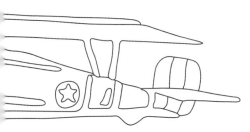

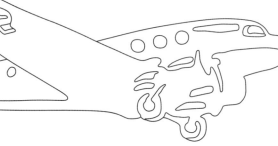

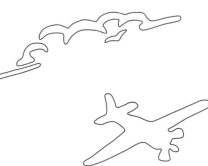

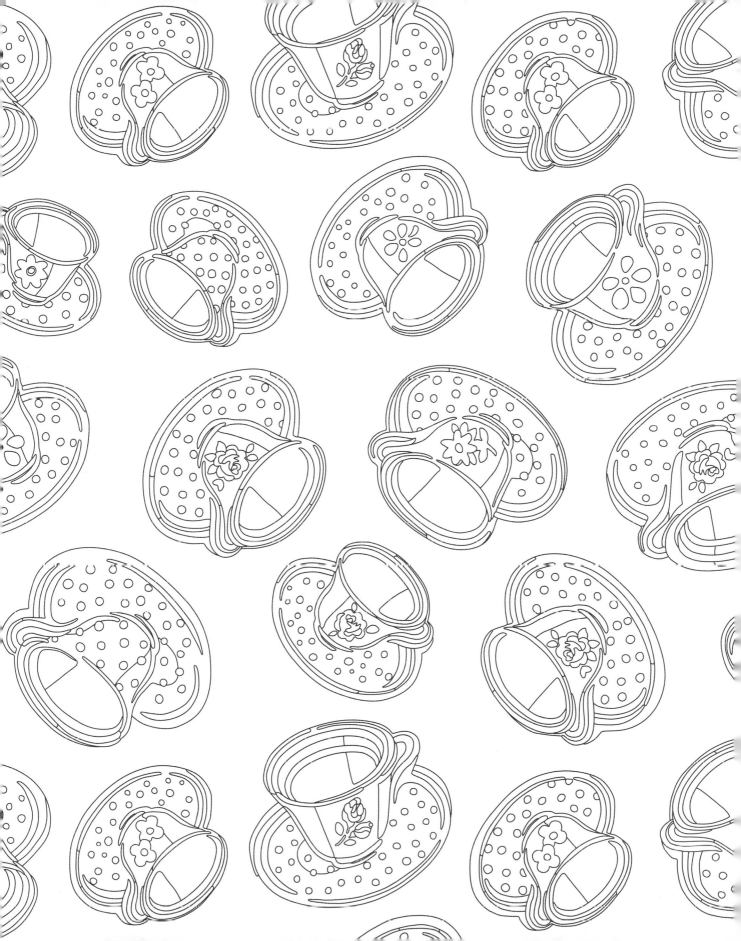

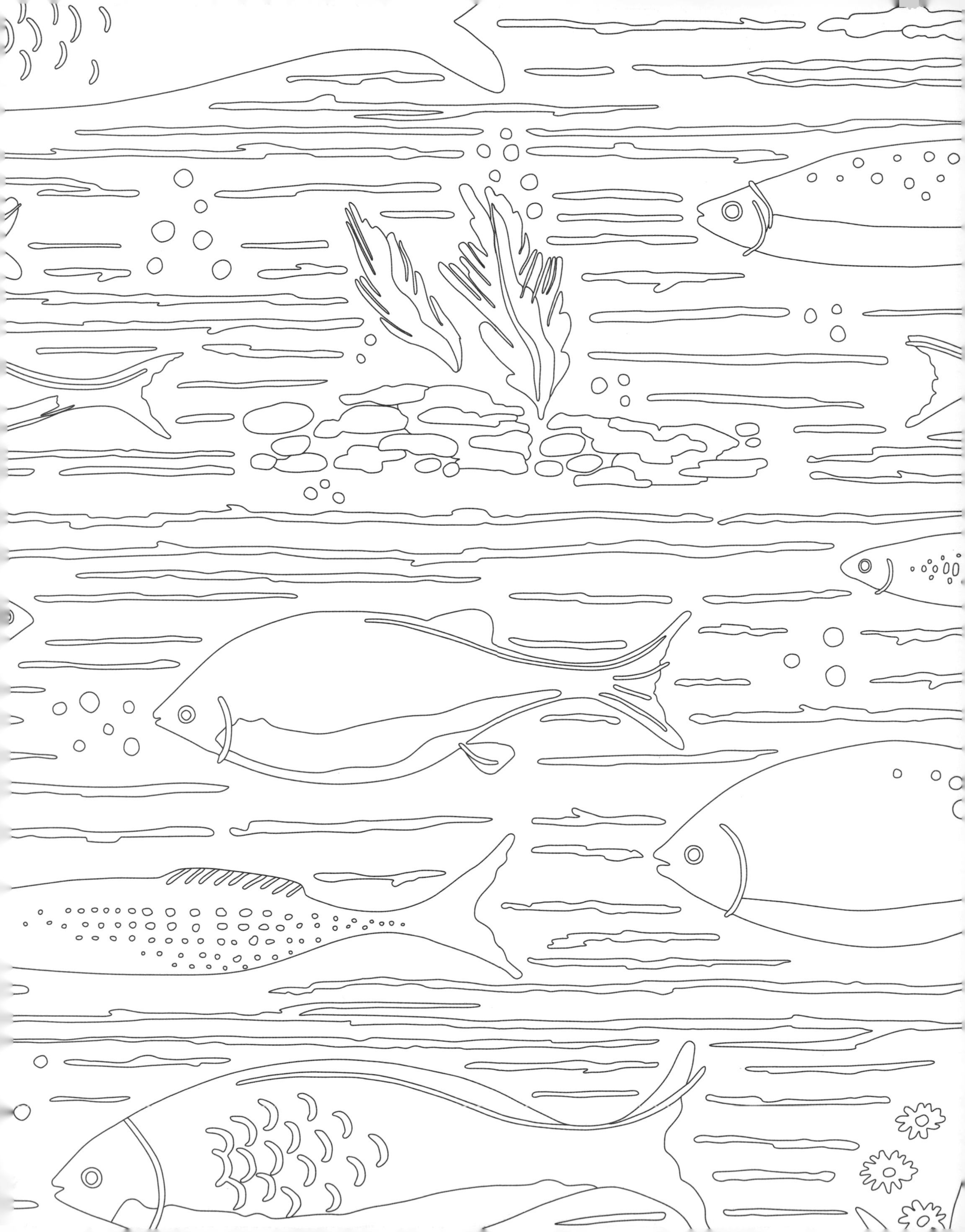

Cath Kidston® Acknowledgements

Special thanks to everyone involved in the making of this book : to Elaine Ashton, Sue Chidler, Dominika Dudziuk, Christine Hafsten, Natasha Hinds-Payne, Gemma Hurley, Victoria Kay, Elisabeth Lester, Lyndsey Nangle, Emma O'Malley, Julie Petges. Anita Povey, Toni Stait and all at Cath Kidston Ltd.

Publishing Director: Sarah Lavelle
Creative Director: Helen Lewis
Editor: Lisa Pendreigh
Editorial Assistant: Harriet Butt
Designer: Gemma Hayden
Illustrator: Sarah Fisher
Production Manager: Stephen Lang
Production Director: Vincent Smith

First published in 2016 by
Quadrille Publishing
Pentagon House
52–54 Southwark Street
London SE1 1UN
www.quadrille.co.uk

Quadrille is an imprint of Hardie Grant
www.hardiegrant.com.au

Reprinted in 2016
10 9 8 7 6 5 4 3 2

Text © 2016 Cath Kidston
Illustrations © 2016 Cath Kidston
Design and layout © 2016 Quadrille Publishing

Cataloguing in Publication Data: a catalogue record for this book is available from the British Library.

ISBN: 978 184949 804 3
Printed in China

For more Cath Kidston products, visit
cathkidston.com